THE BEST OF DAVID BOWIE 1969/1974

Wise Publications
London/New York/Sydney/Paris/Copenhagen/Madrid

THE JEAN GENIE

Small Jean Genie snuck off to the city
Strung out on lasers an' slash-back blazers
And ate all your razors while pulling the waiters
Talking 'bout Monroe and walking on Snow White
New York's a go-go and everything tastes nice
Poor little Greenie

Jean Genie lives on his back
The Jean Genie loves chimney stacks
He's outrageous, he screams and he bawls
Jean Genie let yourself go

Sits like a man but he smiles like a reptile
She loves him, she loves him but just for a short while
She'll scratch in the sand, won't let go his hand
He says he's a beautician and sells you nutrition
And keeps all your dead hair for making up underwear
Poor little Greenie

Jean Genie lives on his back
The Jean Genie loves chimney stacks
He's outrageous, he screams and he bawls
Jean Genie let yourself go

He's so simple minded he can't drive his module
He bites on the neon and sleeps in a capsule
Loves to be loved, loves to be loved

Jean Genie lives on his back
The Jean Genie loves chimney stacks
He's outrageous, he screams and he bawls
Jean Genie let yourself go

SPACE ODDITY

Ground Control to Major Tom
Ground Control to Major Tom
Take your protein pills and put your helmet on

Ground Control to Major Tom
Commencing countdown, engines on
Check ignition and may God's love be with you

Ten Nine Eight Seven Six Five Four Three Two One Liff-off

This is Ground Control to Major Tom
You've really made the grade
And the papers want to know whose shirts you wear
Now it's time to leave the capsule if you dare

This is Major Tom to Ground Control
I'm stepping through the door
And I'm floating in a most peculiar way
And the stars look very different today

For here am I sitting in a tin can
Far above the world
Planet Earth is blue
And there's nothing I can do

Though I'm past one hundred thousand miles
I'm feeling very still
And I think my spaceship knows which way to go
Tell my wife I love her very much, she knows

Ground Control to Major Tom
Your circuit's dead - there's something wrong
Can you hear me Major Tom?
Can you hear me Major Tom?

Here am I floating round my tin can
Far above the Moon
Planet Earth is blue
And there's nothing I can do

STARMAN

Didn't know what time it was
The lights were low
I leaned back on my radio
Some cat was layin' down some rock 'n' roll
Lotta soul he said
Then the loud sound did seem to fade
Came back like a slow voice
On a wave of phase
That weren't no DJ
That was hazy cosmic jive

There's a starman waiting in the sky
He'd like to come and meet us
But he thinks he'll blow our minds
There's a starman waiting in the sky
He's told us not to blow it
'Cause he knows it's all worthwhile
He told me
Let the children lose it
Let the children use it
Let all the children boogie

I had to phone someone
So I picked on you
Hey that's far out so you heard him too
Switch on the TV
We may pick him up on channel two
Look out your window
I can see his light
If we can sparkle he may land tonight
Don't tell your poppa
Or he'll get us locked up in fright

There's a starman waiting in the sky
He'd like to come and meet us
But he thinks he'll blow our minds
There's a starman waiting in the sky
He's told us not to blow it
'Cause he knows it's all worthwhile
He told me
Let the children lose it
Let the children use it
Let all the children boogie

ZIGGY STARDUST

Ziggy played guitar
Jamming good with Weird and Gilly
And the Spiders from Mars
He played it left hand
But made it too far
Became the special man
Then we were Ziggy's band

Ziggy really sang
Screwed up eyes
And screwed down hair-do
Like some cat from Japan
He could lick 'em by smiling
He could leave 'em to hang
They came on so loaded man
Well hung and snowwhite tan

So where were the Spiders
While the fly tried to break our balls?
With just the beer light to guide us
So we bitched about his fans
And should we crush his sweet hands?

Ziggy played for time
Jiving us that we were voodoo
The kids were just crass
He was the nazz
With God given ass
He took it all too far
But boy could he play guitar

Making love with his ego
Ziggy sucked up into his mind
Like a leper messiah
When the kids had killed the man
I had to break up the band

Ziggy played guitar

JOHN, I'M ONLY DANCING

Annie's very sweet
She always eats her meat
And Joey comes on strong
Bet your life he's putting us on

Oh Lawdy, oh Lawdy
You know I need some loving
Hold me, touch me
John I'm only dancing
She turns me on
But I'm only dancing
She turns me on
But don't get me wrong
I'm only dancing

Shadow love is quick and clean
Life's a well thumbed machine
I saw you watching from the stairs
You're everyone that ever cared

Oh Lawdy, Oh Lawdy
You know I need some loving
Hold me, touch me
John I'm only dancing
She turns me on
But I'm only dancing
She turns me on
But don't get me wrong
I'm only dancing

Won't someone dance with me
Touch me

REBEL REBEL

You got your mother in a whirl
She's not sure if you're a boy or a girl
Hey babe your hair's alright
Hey babe let's go out tonight
You like me and I like it all
We like dancing and we look divine
You love bands when they play it hard
You want more and you want it fast
They put you down they say I'm wrong
You tacky thing
You put them on

Rebel rebel you've torn your dress
Rebel rebel your face is a mess
Rebel rebel how could they know?
Hot tramp I love you so

You've torn your dress
Your face is a mess
You can't get enough but enough ain't the test
You've got your transmission and a live wire
You've got your cue lines and a handful of ludes
You wanna be there when they count up the dudes
And I love your dress
You're a juvenile success
Because your face is a mess
So how could they know
I said how could they know?

So what-cha wanna know
Calamity's child? chi-chile, chi-chile
Oh where d'ya wanna go?
What can I do for you?
Looks like I been there too
'Cause you've torn your dress
And your face is a mess
Oo your face is a mess
So how could they know?
How could they know?

LET'S SPEND THE NIGHT TOGETHER

Well, don't you worry 'bout what's been on my mind
I'm in no hurry I can take my time
I'm going red and my tongue's getting tired
I'm off my head and my mouth's getting dry
I'm-a h-h-h-high

Let's spend the night together
Now I need you more than ever
Let's spend the night together now

I feel so strong that I can't disguise, oh my
But, I just can't apologise, no
Don't hang me up but don't let me down
We could have fun just a-fooling around and around

Let's spend the night together
Now I need you more than ever
Let's spend the night together now

You know I'm smiling baby
You need some guiding baby
I'm just deciding baby

Let's spend the night together
Now I need you more than ever
Let's spend the night together now

This doesn't happen to me every day
No excuses I've got anyway, hey
I'll satisfy your every need
And now I know you'll satisfy me, oh my

Let's spend the night together
Now I need you more than ever

They said we were too young
Our kind of love was no fun
But our love comes from above
Do it!
Let's make love

Let's spend the night together
Now I need you more than ever
Let's spend the night together now

SUFFRAGETTE CITY

Hey man, oh leave me alone you know
Hey man, oh Henry get off the phone I gotta
Hey man, I gotta straighten my face
This mellow thighed chick just put my spine out of place

Hey man, my school days insane
Hey man, my work's down the drain
Hey man well she's a total blam-blam
She said she had to squeeze it
But she, and then she

Oh don't lean on me man
'Cause you can't afford the ticket
I'm back on Suffragette City
Oh don't lean on me man
'Cause you ain't got time to check it
You know my Suffragette City is outta sight
She's alright

Hey man, oh Henry don't be unkind go away
Hey man, I can't take you this time no way
Hey man, say droogie don't crash here
There's only room for one
And here she comes, here she comes

Oh don't lean on me man
'Cause you can't afford the ticket
I'm back on Suffragette City
Oh don't lean on me man
'Cause you ain't got time to check it
You know my Suffragette City is outta sight
She's all right, oh hit me

A Suffragette City, Oh wham bam thank you Ma'am! Suffragette!

OH! YOU PRETTY THINGS

Wake up you sleepy head
Put on some clothes, shake up your bed
Put another log on the fire for me
I've made some breakfast and coffee
Look out my window, what do I see?
A crack in the sky and a hand reaching down to me
All the nightmares came today
And it looks as though they're here to stay

What are we coming to?
No room for me, no fun for you
I think about a world to come
Where the books were found by the Golden Ones
Written in pain, written in awe
By a puzzled man who questioned
What we were here for
All the strangers came today
And it looks as though they're here to stay

Oh You Pretty Things
Don't you know you're driving your
Mamas and papas insane?
Oh You Pretty Things
Don't you know you're driving your
Mamas and papas insane?
Let me make it plain
Gotta make way for the Homo Superior

Look out at your children
See their faces in golden rays
Don't kid yourself they belong to you
They're the start of the coming race
The earth is a bitch
We've finished our news
Homo sapiens have outgrown their use
All the strangers came today
And it looks as though they're here to stay

Oh You Pretty Things
Don't you know you're driving your
Mamas and papas insane?
Oh You Pretty Things
Don't you know you're driving your
Mamas and papas insane?
Let me make it plain
Gotta make way for the Homo Superior

VELVET GOLDMINE

You got crazy legs, you got amazin' head
You got rings on your fingers and your hair's hot red
You got the width of my tongue your name on the sun
I clutch you close to my breast
'Cause you're the only one, who uses school to pleasure

You make me act real gone, you make me troll along
I had to ravish your capsule, suck you dry
Feel the teeth in your bones, till your head is my home
If I don't have you whole, is that your final love?
Here all together

Velvet goldmine, you stroke me like the rain
Snake it, take it, panther princess you must stay
Velvet goldmine, naked on your chain
I'll be your king volcano right for you again and again
My velvet goldmine

You're my taste, my trip, I'll be your master zip
I'll chop your hair off for kicks, you'll make me jump to my feet
So you'll give me your hand, give me your sound
Let my sea wash your face, I'm falling, I can't stand
Oooh! Clutch your makeup!

Velvet goldmine, you stroke me like the rain
Snake it, take it, panther princess you must stay
Velvet goldmine, naked on your chain
I'll be your king volcano right for you again and again
My velvet goldmine

Oh
Shoot you down, bang bang

Velvet goldmine, you stroke me like the rain
Snake it, take it, panther princess you must stay
Velvet goldmine, naked on your chain
I'll be your king volcano right for you again and again
My velvet goldmine

DRIVE-IN SATURDAY

Let me put my arms around your head
Gee it's hot let's go to bed
Don't forget to turn on the light
Don't laugh babe it'll be alright
Pour me out another phone
I'll ring and see if your friends are home
Perhaps the strange ones in the dome
Can lend us a book we can read up alone

And try to get it on like once before
When people stared in Jagger's eyes and scored
Like the video films we saw

His name was always Buddy
And he'd shrug and ask to stay
She'd sigh like Twig the Wonder Kid
And turn her face away
She's uncertain if she likes him
But she knows she really loves him
It's a crash course for the ravers
It's a drive-in Saturday

Jung the foreman prayed at work
That neither hands nor limbs would burst
It's hard enough to keep formation
Amid this fall-out saturation
Cursing at the Astronette
That stands in steel by his cabinet
He is crashing out with Sylvian
Bureau supply for ageing men

With snorting head he gazes to the shore
Where once it raged a sea that raged no more
Like the video films we saw

His name was always Buddy
And he'd shrug and ask to stay
And she'd sigh like Twig the Wonder Kid
And turn her face away
She's uncertain if she likes him
But she knows she really loves him
It's a crash course for the ravers
It's a drive-in Saturday

DIAMOND DOGS

This ain't rock 'n' roll
This is genocide!

As they pulled you out of the oxygen tent
You asked for the latest party
With your silicone hump and your ten-inch stump
Dressed like a priest you was
Tod Browning's freak you was

Crawling down the alley on your hands and knee
I'm sure you're not protected
For it's plain to see
The diamond dogs are poachers
And they hide behind trees
Hunt you to the ground they will
Mannequins with kill appeal

Will they come?
I'll keep a friend serene
Will they come?
Oh baby come unto me
Will they come?
Well she's come, been and gone

Come out of the garden baby
You'll catch your death in the fog
Young girl
They call them the diamond dogs
Young girl
They call them the diamond dogs

Now Halloween Jack is a real cool cat
And he lives on top of Manhattan Chase
The elevator's broke
So he slides down a rope
Onto the street below
Oh Tarzie go man go

Meets his little hussy
With his ghost-town approach
Her face is sans feature
But she wears a Dali brooch
Sweetly reminiscent
Something mother used to bake
Wrecked up and paralyzed
Diamond Dogs are sableized

Will they come?
I'll keep a friend serene
Will they come?
Oh baby come unto me
Will they come?
Well she's come, been and gone

Come out of the garden baby
You'll catch your death in the fog
Young girl
They call them the diamond dogs
Young girl
They call them the diamond dogs

In the year of the scavenger
The season of the bitch
Sashay on the broadwalk
Scurry to the ditch
Just another future song
Lonely little kitsch
There's gonna be sorrow
Try and wake up tomorrow

Will they come?
I'll keep a friend serene
Will they come?
Oh baby come unto me
Will they come?
Well she's come, been and gone

Come out of the garden baby
You'll catch your death in the fog
Young girl
They call them the diamond dogs
Young girl
They call them the diamond dogs

CHANGES

Still don't know what I was waiting for
And my time was running wild
A million dead-end streets
And every time I thought I'd got it made
It seemed the taste was not so sweet
So I turned myself to face me
But I've never caught a glimpse
Of how the others must see the faker
I'm much too fast to take that test

Ch-ch-ch-ch-changes
Turn and face the strange changes
Don't want to be a richer man
Ch-ch-ch-ch-changes
Turn and face the strange changes
It's gonna have to be a different man
Time may change me
But I can't trace time

I watch the ripples change their size
But never leave the stream
Of warm impermanence
So the days float thru' my eyes
But still the days seem the same
And these children that you spit on
As they try to change their worlds
Are immune to your consultations
They're quite aware of what they're going thru'

Ch-ch-ch-ch-changes
Turn and face the strange changes
Don't tell them to grow up and out of it
Ch-ch-ch-ch-changes
Turn and face the strange changes
Where's your shame
You've left us up to our necks in it
Time may change me
But you can't trace time

Strange fascination, fascinating me
Oh changes are taking the pace I'm going thru'

Ch-ch-ch-ch-changes
Turn and face the strange changes
Ooh look out you rock and rollers
Ch-ch-ch-ch-changes
Turn and face the strange changes
Pretty soon now you're gonna get older
Time may change me
But I can't trace time
I said that time may change me
But I can't trace time

SORROW

With your long blonde hair and your eyes of blue
The only thing I ever got from you
Was sorrow - sorrow

You acted funny, tryin' to spend my money
You're out there playing your high class games
Of sorrow - sorrow

You never do what you know you oughta
Something tells me you're the devil's daughter
Sorrow - sorrow

I tried to find her 'cos I can't resist her
I never knew just how much I miss her
Sorrow - sorrow

With your long blonde hair and your eyes of blue
The only thing I ever got from you
Was sorrow - sorrow

With your long blonde hair
I couldn't sleep last night
With your long blonde hair

THE PRETTIEST STAR

Cold fire, you got everything but cold fire
You will be my rest and peace child
I moved up to take a place near you

So tired, it's the sky that makes you feel tired
It's a trick to make you see wide
It can all but break your heart in pieces

Staying back in your memory
Are the movies in the dark
How you move is all it takes
To sing a song of when I loved
The prettiest star

Staying back in your memory
Are the movies in the dark
How you move is all it takes
To sing a song of when I loved
The prettiest star

One day though it might as well be someday
You will rise up high and take us all away
All because of what you are
The prettiest star

LIFE ON MARS?

It's a God-awful small affair
To the girl with the mousy hair
But her mummy is yelling 'No!'
And her daddy has told her to go
But her friend is nowhere to be seen
Now she walks through her sunken dream
To the seat with the clearest view
And she's hooked to the silver screen
But the film is a sadd'ning bore
For she's lived it ten times or more
She could spit in the eyes of fools
As they ask her to focus on
Sailors fighting in the dance hall
Oh man, look at those cavemen go
It's the freakiest show
Take a look at the lawman
Beating up the wrong guy
Oh man wonder if he'll ever know
He's in the best selling show
Is there life on Mars?

It's on Amerika's tortured brow
That Mickey Mouse has grown up a cow
Now the workers have struck for fame
'Coz Lennon's on sale again
See the mice in their million hordes
From Ibiza to the Norfolk Broads
Rule Bnttania is out of bounds
To my mother, my dog, and clowns
But the film is a sadd'ning bore
'Coz I wrote it ten times or more
It's about to be writ again
As I ask her to focus on
Sailors fighting in the dance hall
Oh man, look at those cavemen go
It's the freakiest show
Take a look at the lawman
Beating up the wrong guy
Oh man wonder if he'll ever know
He's in the best selling show
Is there life on Mars?

ALADDIN SANE

Watching him dash away, swinging an old bouquet of dead roses
Sake and strange divine Uh-h-h-uh-h-uh you'll make it
Passionate bright young things, takes him away to war - don't fake it
Saddening glissando strings
Uh-h-h-uh-h-uh - you'll make it

Who will love Aladdin Sane?
Battle cries and champagne just in time for sunrise
Who will love Aladdin Sane?

Motor sensational, Paris or maybe hell - I'm waiting
Clutches of sad remains
Waits for Aladdin Sane - you'll make it

Who will love Aladdin Sane
Millions weep a fountain, just in case of sunrise
Who will love Aladdin Sane

Will love Aladdin Sane?
Will love Aladdin Sane?

Who will love Aladdin Sane?
Millions weep a fountain, just in case of sunrise
Who will love Aladdin Sane?

Will love Aladdin Sane?
Will love Aladdin Sane?

ROCK 'N' ROLL SUICIDE

Time takes a cigarette
Puts it in your mouth
You pull on your finger
Then another finger
Then your cigarette
The wall to wall is calling
It lingers
Then you forget
Oh you're a rock 'n' roll suicide

You're too old to lose it
Too young to choose it
And the clock waits so patiently on your song
You walk past the cafe
But you don't eat when you've lived too long
Oh no no no
You're a rock 'n' roll suicide

Chev brakes are snarling
As you stumble across the road
But the day breaks instead
So you hurry home
Don't let the sun blast your shadow
Don't let the milk-float ride your mind
They're so natural
Religiously unkind

Oh no love! You're not alone
You're watching yourself
But you're too unfair
You got your head all tangled up
But if I could only make you care

Oh no love! You're not alone
No matter what or who you've been
No matter when or where you've seen
All the knives seem to lacerate your brain
I've had my share
I'll help you with the pain

You're not alone
Just turn on with me
And you're not alone
Let's turn on and be not alone
Gimme your hands 'coz you're wonderful
Gimme your hands 'coz you're wonderful
Oh gimme your hands

ALL THE YOUNG DUDES

Billy rapped all night about his suicide
How he'd kick it in the head when he was twenty five
Don't wanna stay alive when you're twenty five

Wendy's stealing clothes from unlocked cars
And Freddy's got spots from ripping off stars from his face
A funky little boat race
The television man is crazy
Saying we're juvenile delinquent wrecks
Man I need a TV when I've got T. Rex
Hey brother you guessed
I'm a dude

All the young dudes
Carry the news
Boogaloo dudes
Carry the news

Now Jimmy looking sweet though he dresses like a queen
He can kick like a mule
It's a real mean team
We can love
Oh we can love
And my brother's back at home
With his Beatles and his Stones
We never got if off on that revolution stuff
What a drag
Too many snags
Well I drunk a lot of wine
And I'm feeling fine
Gonna race some cat to bed
Is this concrete all around
Or is it in my head?
Oh brother you guessed
I'm a dude

All the young dudes
Carry the news
Boogaloo dudes
Carry the news

THE MAN WHO SOLD THE WORLD

We passed upon the stair, we spoke of was and when
Although I wasn't there, he said I was his friend
Which came as some surprise I spoke into his eyes
I thought you died alone, a long long time ago

Oh no, not me
I never lost control
You're face to face
With the man who sold the world

I laughed and shook his hand, and made my way back home
I searched for form and land, for years and years I roamed
I gazed a gazely stare at all the millions here
We must have died alone, a long long time ago

Who knows? not me
We never lost control
You're face to face
With the man who sold the world

THE JEAN GENIE

Words & Music by David Bowie

1. Small Jean Ge-nie snuck off to the ci-ty, strung out on la-sers and
(Verse 2 see block lyric)

slash-back bla-zers and ate all your ra-zors while pull-ing the wai-ters.

loves chim-ney stacks.___ He's out-ra-geous, he screams and he bawls.___

Jean Ge - nie,___ let your-self go!___

3. He's

so sim-ple mind-ed, he can't drive his mo-dule, he bites on___ the ne-on,___ and

sleeps in a cap-sule.   Loves to be loved,_____

loves to be loved._____

Oh

Jean Ge-nie lives on his back.— The Jean Ge-nie loves—

chim-ney stacks.— He's out-ra-geous, he screams and he bawls.—

Jean Ge-nie, let your-self go!—

Go!— Go!—

Verse 2:
Sits like a man but he smiles like a reptile
She loves him, she loves him but just for a short while
She'll scratch in the sand, won't let go his hand
He says he's a beautician and sells you nutrition
And keeps all your dead hair for making up underwear
Poor Little Greenie, ooh!

SPACE ODDITY

Words & Music by David Bowie

Ground Con-trol— to Ma - jor Tom,—

Ground Con-trol— to Ma - jor Tom,—

take your pro - tein pills and put your hel - met on.___

Ground Con - trol___ to Ma - jor Tom,___

Ten   *Nine*   *Eight*   *Seven*

com - menc - ing count - down, en - gines on,   check ig - ni - tion and may

Six   *Five*   *Four*   *Three*   *Two*   *One*

God's love be with you.___

lift-off.

I'm step - ping through the door, _____ and I'm

float - ing in a most__ pe - cu - li - ar way, _____ and the stars__

_____ look ve - ry dif - fer - ent to - day. _____ For

here am I sit - ting in a tin can, _____
(℆) (float - ing round my)

far ___ a - bove ___ the world. ___
(the moon. ___)

Pla - net Earth ___ is blue and there's no-thing I can do. ___

19

STARMAN

Words & Music by David Bowie

24

2.

Star - man wait-ing in — the sky, he'd like to come — and meet us but he

thinks he'll blow our minds. There's a star - man wait-ing in — the sky, he's

told us not to blow it 'cause he knows — it's all worth-while. He told — me, —

'Let the chil - dren lose it,—— let the chil - dren use it,—— let all the chil - dren boo - gie.'

La la—— la la la la— la la la la— la la la la— la la.

Verse 2:
I had to phone someone so I picked on you
Hey, that's far out so you heard him too!
Switch on the T.V. we may pick him up on channel two
Look out your window, I can see his light
If we can sparkle he may land tonight
Don't tell your poppa or he'll get us locked up in fright.

There's a starman *etc.*

JOHN, I'M ONLY DANCING

Words & Music by David Bowie

1. An-nie's ve - ry sweet she al - ways eats— her meat and Jo - ey comes— on strong,
(Verse 2 see block lyric)

bet your life he's put - ting us on. Oh Lawd - y, oh Lawd - y,

you know___ I   need   some lov-ing.   Hold___ me,

touch___ me.

John,   I'm on-ly danc   -   ing.___   She turns___ me on___

___   but I'm on-ly danc   -   ing.___   She turns___ me on___

She turns___ me on___ but don't get me wrong,___

I'm on - ly danc - ing.___

Danc - ing.___

Won't some - one dance with me.

Verse 2:

Shadow love is quick and clean
Life's a well-thumbed machine
I saw you watching from the stairs
You're everyone that ever cared.
Oh Lawdy, oh Lawdy
You know I need some loving
Hold me, touch me.

John, I'm only dancing *etc.*

ZIGGY STARDUST

Words & Music by David Bowie

Zig-gy played gui-tar,— jam-ming good—with Weird and Gil-ly, and The Spi-ders from Mars.

He played it left hand,___ but made it too far,___

___ be - came_ the spe - cial man,_ then we were Zig-gy's band.__

Zig-gy real-ly sang,___ screwed up eyes_ and screwed down hair - do, like some cat from Ja - pan.

(2° see block lyric)

___ He could lick 'em by smil - ing, he could leave 'em to hang.___ They came on so

Mm._____

1.

Oh   yeah.____   Ooh.____

Free time

Zig - gy played gui - tar.____

2°
Ziggy played for time
Jiving us that we were Voodoo
The Kids were just crass
He was the nazz
With God-given ass
He took it all too far
But boy, could he play guitar.

Making love with his ego
Ziggy sucked up into his mind
Like a leper Messiah
When the kids had killed the man
I had to break up the band.

REBEL REBEL

Words & Music by David Bowie

1. You got your Moth-er in a whirl,— she's not sure if you're a
(Verse 2 see block lyric)

boy or a girl.— Hey babe, your hair's al - right.—

Hey babe, let's go out to - night.— You like me and I

like it all.— We like dan-cing and we look di - vine.—

Reb-el reb-el, how could they know?— Hot tramp, I

love you so.—— Don't ya.

Do do do do

do do do do.

Do do do do do do do do. Reb-el reb-el, you've

torn your dress.— Reb-el reb-el, your face is a mess.—

Reb-el reb-el, how could they know?— Hot tramp, I

love you so.——

how could they know?——

How could they know?——

Do do do do do do do do.

Verse 2:
You got your mother in a whirl
Cos she's not sure if you're a boy or a girl
Hey babe, your hair's alright
Hey babe, let's stay out tonight
You like me and I like it all.
We like dancing and we look divine
You love bands when they play it hard
You want more and you want it fast.

They put you down, they say I'm wrong
You tacky thing, you put them on
Rebel rebel, you've torn your dress
Rebel rebel, your face is a mess
Rebel rebel, how could they know?
Hot tramp I love you so.

SUFFRAGETTE CITY

Words & Music by David Bowie

Hey man, oh,— leave me a-lone,— you know,

hey man, oh Hen-ry get off the phone,— I got-ta, hey man, I got-ta

straight-en my face,___ this mel-low thighed chick___ just put my spine out of place.___

Hey man,___ my school-days in-sane,___ hey man,___ my
(2° see block lyric)

work's down the drain,_____ hey man,___ well she's a to-tal blam-blam,___ she

said she had to squeeze it but she,___ and then she. Oh,___ don't___

lean on me man 'cause you can't af - ford the tick-et.   I'm back on Suf - fra - gette Ci -

- ty.   Oh, don't   lean   on me man 'cause you ain't got time   to check it.

You know my Suf - fra - gette Ci - ty   is out - ta sight.   She's al -

1.

- right.   Mm._____

50

A Suf - fra - gette.

Oh,————— wham   bam   thank - you Mam!

Suf - fra - gette.

2⁰
Hey man, oh Henry don't be unkind, go away
Hey man, I can't take you this time, no way
Hey man, say Droogie don't crash here
There's only room for one and here she comes, here she comes.

Oh don't lean on me *etc.*

LET'S SPEND THE NIGHT TOGETHER

Words & Music by Mick Jagger & Keith Richards

1. Well don't you wor-ry 'bout
(Verses 2 & 3 see block lyrics)

what's been on —— my mind, —

I'm in no hur - ry, I can take my time.

I'm go - ing red and my tongue's get - ting

tired. I'm off my head

and my mouth's get - ting dry, I'm - a h-h-h- h -high.

D.℠. al Coda

⊕ *Coda*

let's spend the night___ to-geth-er,___ now I need you more__

___ than ev-er.___ Let's spend the night___ to-geth-er,___

now I need you more__ then ev-er,___ let's spend the night__

___ to-geth-er.___ They said we were too young, our kind of

Instrumental ad lib.

N.C.

Verse 2:
I feel so strong that I can't disguise, oh my
But I just can't apologise, no
Don't hang me up, but don't let me down
We could have fun Just a-fooling around and around.

Let's spend the night together *etc.*

Verse 3:
This doesn't happen to me every day
No excuses I've got anyway, hey
I'll satisfy your every need
And now I know you'll satisfy me, oh my.

Let's spend the night together *etc.*

OH! YOU PRETTY THINGS

Words & Music by David Bowie

put on some clothes, shake up your bed, put a-no-ther log on the fire for me,

No room for me, no fun— for you, I think a-bout a world— to come,—where the
(2° see block lyrics)

books were found— by the Gol-den Ones,— writ-ten in pain,— writ-ten in awe,— by a—

—— puz-zled man who ques-tioned what we were here for.— All the stran-gers—— came to-

-day, and it looks as though they're here—— to stay.——

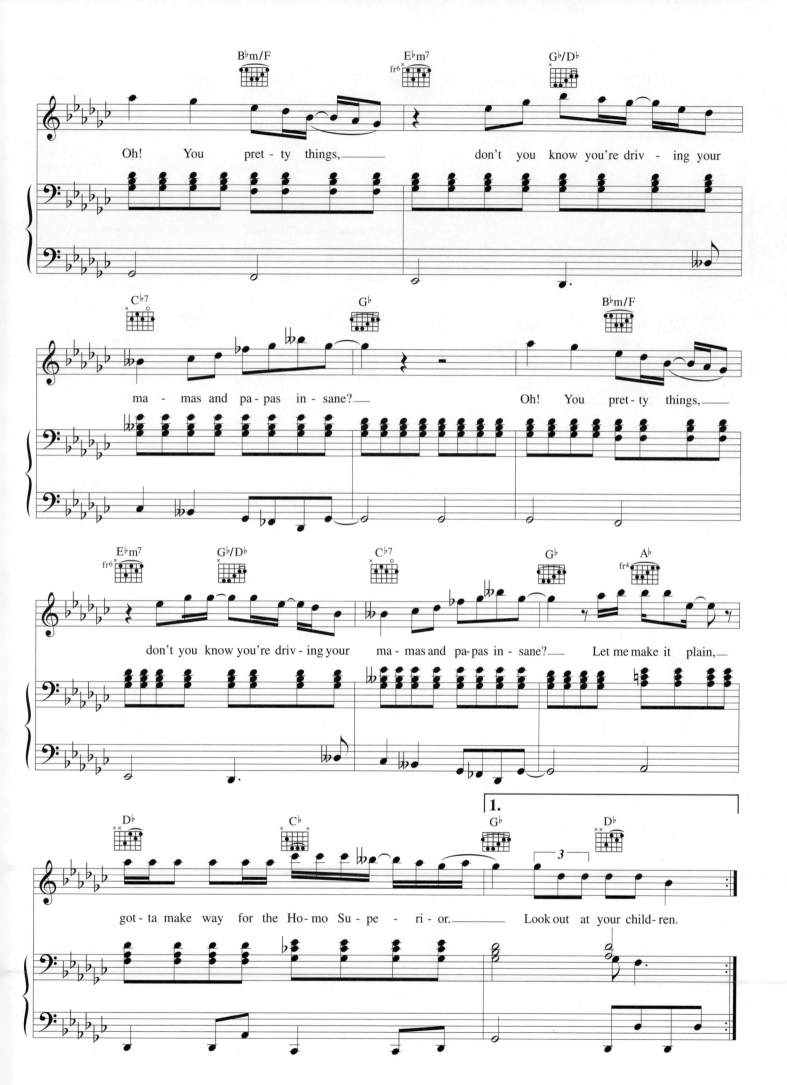

2°:

Look out at your children
See their faces in golden rays
Don't kid yourself they belong to you
They're the start of the coming race.

The earth is a bitch
We've finished our news
Homo sapiens have outgrown their use.
All the strangers came today
And it looks as though they're here to stay.

Oh! You pretty things *etc.*

SORROW

Words & Music by Bob Feldman, Jerry Goldstein & Richard Gottehrer

With your long blond hair and your eyes of blue, the on-ly thing I ev-er got from you was

sor - row,— sor - row.— You

act - ed fun - ny tryin' to spend my mo - ney, you're out there play - ing your—
(2° see block lyric)

high class games of sor - row,—

sor - row.— You nev - er do what you

know you ought - a,   some - thing tells— me you're the   de - vil's daught - er.

Sor - row,—   sor - row.—

Ooh.————————

With your long blonde hair I could-n't

sleep last night. With your long blonde hair.

Repeat ad lib. to fade

2°:
I tried to find her
'Cos I can't resist her
I never knew just how much I miss her
Sorrow, sorrow.

With your long blond hair
And your eyes of blue
The only thing I ever got from you
Was sorrow, sorrow.

VELVET GOLDMINE

Words & Music by David Bowie

you must stay.— Vel - vet gold - mine, na - ked on— your chain.— I'll

be your King Vol - ca - no, right for you a - gain— and a - gain. My vel - vet gold - mine.

1. **2.**

2. You're my Oh

shoot you down bang— bang. Vel - vet

Verse 2:
You're my taste, my trip
I'll be your master zip
I'll chop your hair off for kicks
You'll make me jump to my feet
So you'll give me your hand
Give me your sound
Let my sea wash your face, I'm falling, I can't stand
Ooh, clutch your make-up.

Velvet goldmine *etc.*

DRIVE-IN SATURDAY

Words & Music by David Bowie

To Coda ⊕

name was al-ways Bud-dy and he'd shrug and ask to stay.— She'd

sigh like— Twig the Won-der Kid and turn her face a-way.— She's un-

-cer-tain if she likes him but she knows she real-ly loves him. It's a crash course—for the rav-ers, it's a

drive - - - in— Sa - tur - day.——

74

Verse 2:
Jung the foreman prayed at work
That neither hands nor limbs would burst
It's hard enough to keep formation
Amid this fall out saturation
Cursing at the Astronette
That stands in steel by his cabinet
He is crashing out with Sylvian
Bureau supply for ageing men
With snorting head he gazes to the shore
Where once it raged, the sea that raged no more
Like the video films we saw.

His name was always Buddy *etc.*

DIAMOND DOGS

Words & Music by David Bowie

Spoken: This ain't rock 'n' roll. This is genocide!

1. As they

pulled you out___ of the ox - y - gen tent___ you asked for the la - test par -
(Verse 2 see block lyric)

-ty. With your si - li - cone hump and your ten___ inch stump,___

dressed like a priest you was,___ Tod Brown-ing's freak you was.___ Crawl-ing down the al- ley on your
(℀ see block lyric)

hands and knee,___ I'm sure you're not pro- tect - ed for it's___ plain to see___ the

Repeat ad lib. to fade

Be - ware   of the dia - mond dogs.

Verse 2:
Now Halloween Jack is a real cool cat
And he lives on top of Manhattan Chase
The elevators broke so he slides down a rope
Onto the street below, oh Tarzie go man, go.
Meet his little hussy with his ghost town approach
Her face is sans feature but she wears a Dali brooch
Sweetly reminiscent, something Mother used to bake
Wrecked up and paralyzed, diamond dogs are sableized.

(Will they come?) *etc.*

On 𝄋:
In the year of the scavenger, the season of the bitch
Sashay on the broadwalk, scurry to the ditch
Just another future song, lonely little kitsch
(There's gonna be sorrow) Try and wake up tomorrow.

(Will they come?) *etc.*

CHANGES

Words & Music by David Bowie

1. Still don't know what I___ was wait-ing for, and my
(Verse 2 see block lyric)

time was run-ning wild,___ a mil-lion dead end streets, and ev-'ry time I thought I'd

got it made___ it seemed the taste was not so sweet. So I

turned my - self to face me,___ but I've nev - er caught a glimpse

of how the oth - ers must see___ the fa - ker, I'm much too

Verse 2:

I watch the ripples change their size
But never leave the stream of warm impermanence
So the days float thru' my eyes
But still the days seem the same.

And these children that you spit on
As they try to change their worlds
Are immune to your consultations
They're quite aware of what they're going thru'.

Ch-ch-ch-ch-changes
Turn and face the strange
Ch-ch-changes
Don't tell them to grow up and out of it.
Ch-ch-ch-ch-changes
Turn and face the strange
Ch-ch-changes
Where's your shame
You've left us up to our necks in it
Time may change me
But you can't trace time.

THE PRETTIEST STAR

Words & Music by David Bowie

Cold fire,— you got ev-'ry-thing— but cold— fire.

someday,—— you will rise—— up high and take us all a-way.

All be-cause of what you are, the pret-ti-est—— star.

Repeat ad lib. to fade

LIFE ON MARS?

Words & Music by David Bowie

beat-ing up the wrong guy.   Oh, man,   won-der if he'll ev-er know

he's in the best sell-ing show.

Is there life on Mars?

To Coda

Verse 2:

It's on Amerika's tortured brow that Mickey Mouse has grown up a cow
Now the workers have struck for fame coz Lennon's on sale again
See the mice in their million hordes, from Ibiza to the Norfolk Broads
Rule Brittania is out of bounds to my mother, my dog and clowns
But the film is a saddening bore coz I wrote it ten times or more
It's about to be writ again as I ask her to focus on.

Sailors fighting in the dance hall *etc.*

ALADDIN SANE

Words & Music by David Bowie

Verse 2:
Passionate bright young things
Takes him away to war, don't fake it
Saddening glissando strings
Uh uh uh uh uh uh, you'll make it.

Who will love *etc.*

Verse 3:
Motor sensational
Paris or maybe Hell, I'm waiting
Clutches of sad remains
Waits for Aladdin Sane, you'll make it.

Who will love *etc.*

THE MAN WHO SOLD THE WORLD

Words & Music by David Bowie

1. We passed up - on the stair, we

(Verse 2 see block lyric)

spoke of was and when. Al - though I was - n't there

sim.

2. I laughed and shook his

Who knows

Verse 2:
I laughed and shook his hand
And made my way back home.
I searched for form and land
For years and years I roamed
I gazed a gazely stare
At all the millions here
We must have died alone
A long, long time ago.

Who knows? Not me
We never lost control
You're face to face
With the man who sold the world.

ROCK 'N' ROLL SUICIDE

Words & Music by David Bowie

but you're too—un-fair. You got your head all tan-gled up, but if I could on-ly

make you care.— Oh— no love, you're not a-lone,— no mat-ter

what or who you've been,— no mat-ter when or where you've seen.— All the

knives seem to la-cer-ate your brain, I've had my share, I'll help you with the pain.

You're not a-lone.——

Just turn on with me and you're not a-lone.——

Let's turn on and be not a-lone.

Gim-me your hands coz you're won-der-ful.

114

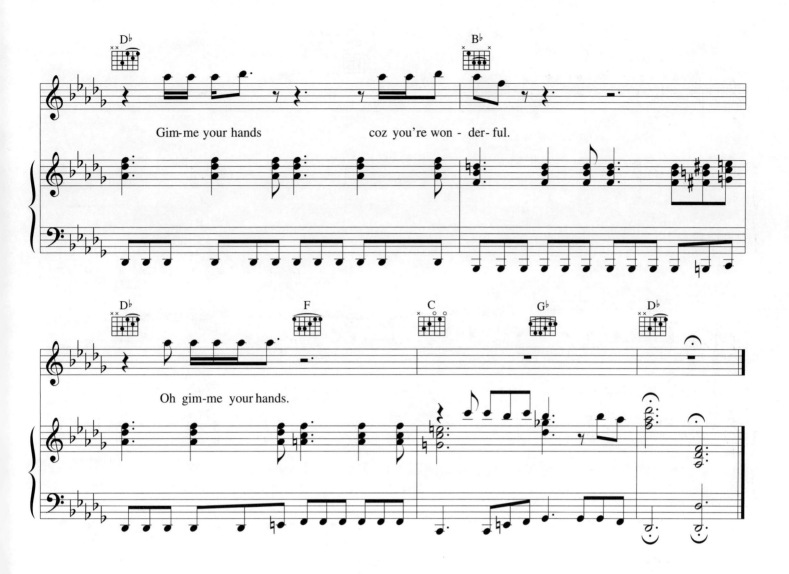

Gim-me your hands   coz you're won - der- ful.

Oh gim-me your hands.

Verse 2:
You're too old to lose it
Too young to choose it
And the clock waits so patiently on your song
You walk past the café
But you don't eat when you've lived too long
Oh no, no, no
You're a rock 'n' roll suicide.

All the Young Dudes

Words & Music by David Bowie

rapped all night a-bout his su - i - cide,_ how he'd kick it in the head when he was twen-ty five.
(Verse 2 see block lyric)

Verse 2:

Now Jimmy looking sweet though he dresses like a queen
He can kick like a mule, it's a real mean team
We can love
Oh we can love
And my brother's back at home with his Beatles and his Stones
We never got it off on that revolution stuff
What a drag
Too many snags.
Well I drunk a lot of wine and I'm feeling fine
Gonna race some cat to bed
Is this concrete all around or is it in my head?
Oh brother you guessed, I'm a dude.

All the young dudes *etc.*

Exclusive Distributors:
Music Sales Limited
8/9 Frith Street,
London W1V 5TZ, England.
Music Sales Pty Limited
120 Rothschild Avenue
Rosebery, NSW 2018,
Australia.

Order No.AM954459
ISBN 0-7119-7253-2
This book © Copyright 1998
by Wise Publications.
Visit the Internet Music Shop at
http://www.musicsales.co.uk

Music arranged by Derek Jones.
Music processed by Paul Ewers Music Design.

Printed in the United Kingdom by
Redwood Books Ltd, Trowbridge, Wiltshire.

Your Guarantee of Quality:
As publishers, we strive to produce every
book to the highest commercial standards.
The music has been freshly engraved and,
whilst endeavouring to retain the original
running order of the recorded album,
the book has been carefully designed
to minimise awkward page turns and
to make playing from it a real pleasure.
Particular care has been given to specifying
acid-free, neutral-sized paper made
from pulps which have not been elemental
chlorine bleached.
This pulp is from farmed sustainable
forests and was produced with special
regard for the environment.
Throughout, the printing and binding have
been planned to ensure a sturdy, attractive
publication which should give years
of enjoyment.
If your copy fails to meet our high standards,
please inform us and we will gladly replace it.

Music Sales' complete catalogue
describes thousands of titles and is available
in full colour sections by subject, direct from
Music Sales Limited.
Please state your areas of interest and send a
cheque/postal order for £1.50 for postage to:
Music Sales Limited, Newmarket Road,
Bury St. Edmunds, Suffolk IP33 3YB.